This book belongs to

Other Archibald Koala books by Paul Cox

The Riddle of the Floating Island

This edition first published in Great Britain in 1992 by
Jonathan Cape Ltd,
20 Vauxhall Bridge Road, London SW1V 2SA

A CIP catalogue for this book
is available from the British Library

ISBN 0 224 03564 9

Printed and bound in France

The Great Eucalyptus Mystery

Paul Cox

The Adventures of Archibald Koala

The Great Eucalyptus Mystery

Jonathan Cape
London

1

In the middle of the Pacific Ocean is a small island called Wombalano.

The only creatures living on this island are koalas and badgers. The koalas discovered Wombalano more than two hundred years ago and built a small town called Koalaville on its west coast.

The badgers, who arrived

at the same time, settled in the east and named their small town Badgerville.

This is a map of the island:

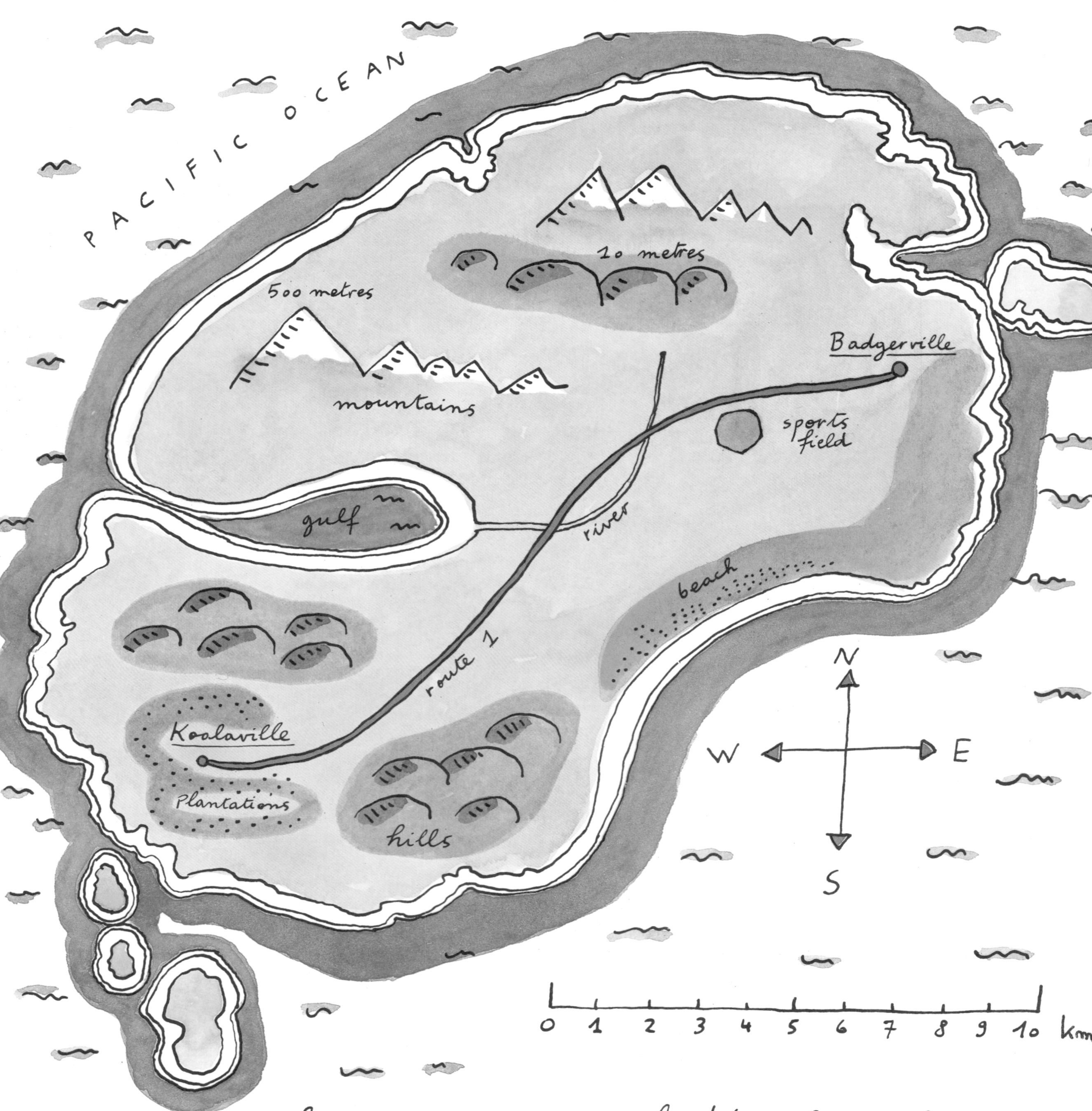

Today the population of Koalaville is twenty-five, made up of the following:

Our hero, Archibald, a private detective, his wife Archibaldine and their three children;

Archie Tect, who, as his name suggests, builds houses in and around Koalaville, his wife and their two children;

Archie Duke, mayor of the island
his wife, and their four children;

Archie Vist, historian and man of letters,
his wife, and their three children;

and last of all Archisoufflé, chef and owner of a three-star restaurant in the centre of Koalaville, his wife, and their three children. These are the twenty-five inhabitants of Koalaville.

Badgerville also has a population of twenty-five: Badgenius, professor of Latin and Greek, his wife, and their one daughter;

Badjellyfish, the fisherman, his wife, and their five children;

Badgick Carpet, the antique dealer, his wife, and their two children;

Badgiovanni, the opera singer, his wife, and their four children;

and lastly Badgibberish, the printer and editor of The Wombalano Times, his wife, and their three children.

Until recently, all was well between the koalas and the badgers on the island of Wombalano. The inhabitants of Koalaville

and Badgerville often met for basketball and rugby games, which they played in their own way, using two balls at the same time, on a curious octagonal pitch.

There is only one town hall in Wombalano. It is in Koalaville, where all government business is conducted.

Archie Duke the mayor, assisted by his very efficient deputy Archibald, was loved and respected by all.

The Badgervillians often dined out in Koalaville at chef Archisoufflé's restaurant, and the Koalavillians had many a memorable evening at the Badgerville opera.

But recently times had not been as happy in Wombalano. The koalas and the badgers were not getting along together at all well. And this is why:

Everyone knows that koalas only eat eucalyptus leaves. In fact, the whole countryside around Koalaville is planted with eucalyptus trees.

Chef Archisoufflé uses the leaves in a hundred different recipes.

To give you an idea of his flair here is a typical menu:

Menu

*

* *

Sautéed eucalyptus leaves
with vinaigrette dressing

*

Eucalyptus leaf casserole
smothered in a eucalyptus sauce

*

Warm eucalyptus soup
served with pitted olives
stuffed with eucalyptus leaves

*

Eucalyptus ice cream
topped with eucalyptus syrup

*

* *

Now the badgers had dined so often at Archisoufflé's restaurant that they were running out of money. So they thought up a cunning scheme. They would steal the koalas' eucalyptus leaves, turn them into chewing gum, and export it to the United States of America!

So after dark every Sunday night, while the unsuspecting koalas were staying quietly in their homes, the badgers headed for the outskirts of Koalaville, then crept back with their sacks full of eucalyptus leaves.

Badjellyfish and Badgiovanni were in charge of these expeditions, assisted by their wives and children.

16
As for Badgick Carpet, it was his job to turn
the eucalyptus leaves into chewing gum. He and his wife worked in the back room of their antique shop, which they had transformed into a chewing gum factory.
Badgibberish took care of the labels and packing materials. He ran them off secretly on his printing press after the late edition of The Wombalano Times.
THIS WAY UP
FRAGILE

Badgenius, who had beautiful handwriting, wrote out the bills for the chewing gum while his wife licked the stamps and stuck them on to the packages.

The koalas soon became alarmed. Every week they found to their horror that their eucalyptus trees had fewer and fewer leaves.

"What will become of us if this carries on?" sighed Archie Duke the mayor.

"What will I serve my customers?" wailed Archisoufflé.

They all scratched their heads, trying to think of a solution to the problem, which was not easy, since they did not know the cause of it!

"Our trees must be sick," said Archie Vist, and he plunged into his history books to see if such a thing had ever happened before. But search as he might, he could find nothing.

Archisoufflé concocted various new fertilizers, mainly made of vitamins, chocolate, and eucalyptus leaves. But nothing worked. Each week the eucalyptus trees lost more and more leaves.

Archisoufflé →
giving the trees fertilizer.

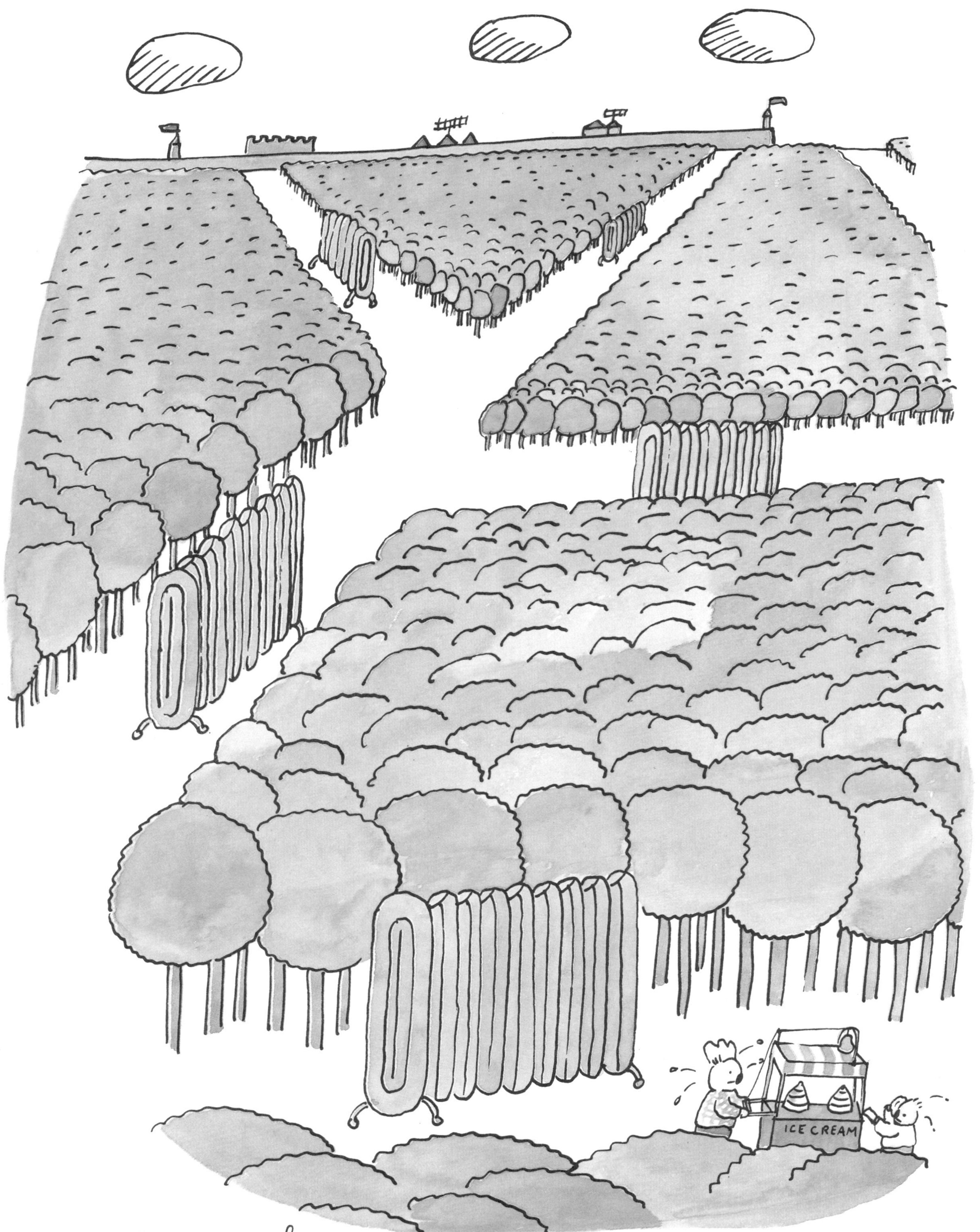

"Perhaps they are cold," suggested Archibald. So Archie Duke the mayor quickly arranged for large radiators to be installed among the trees. But that didn't work either.

"Then they must be too hot," thought Archibald. They replaced the radiators with huge fans. But all their efforts were in vain.

It was at this point that Archibald noticed a very significant fact: while the eucalyptus trees were certainly losing their leaves, none of the leaves were lying on the ground.

"Maybe there are rodents up in the mountains who come down to chew up our trees," he thought. He told his idea to Archie Duke the mayor, who immediately asked Archie Tect to build a high wall around the trees.

But the walls did not stop the badgers. They were extremely good at digging holes! So every Sunday night Badjellyfish and Badgiovanni, helped by their wives and children,

dug little tunnels beneath the wall right up to the foot of the eucalyptus trees. Then they crept back the same way with their bundles, carefully covering their tracks as they went.

Months went by and the inhabitants of Koalaville were becoming more and more desperate. Archisoufflé ran out of food and was forced to close his three-star restaurant.

The badgers, on the other hand, became richer and richer on the growing success of their eucalyptus chewing gum.

One day Badgibberish, Badgenius, Badjellyfish, Badgiovanni and Badgick Carpet drove up to the town hall in Koalaville, with great pomp, in the super de luxe limousines they had bought with their ill-gotten gains.

Badgibberish addressed Archie Duke the mayor on behalf of his fellow badgers: "My poor Archie Duke, you chaps in Koalaville seem to be in a spot of trouble. We badgers on the other hand are getting richer by the day. What we propose is this: we buy Koalaville from you, and I myself, with the full support of all the Badgervillians, will become king of Wombalano."

But the badgers' visit to the town hall made the ever observant Archibald very suspicious. "What if all this sudden wealth has something to do with our eucalyptus trees?" he mused.

He decided to stand guard over the ill-fated trees from morning to night and from night until morning. He began his watch first thing on a Monday, hidden behind a small mound. He had a pair of infra-red binoculars that could see through the dark, a picnic hamper and a flask of hot chocolate.

For seven days and six nights Archibald saw nothing. Then on the seventh night he spied, only a few yards away, Badgiovanni and Badjellyfish appearing from out of the ground, followed by their wives and children.

In no time at all some had climbed to the top of the trees while the others stuffed the leaves into big sacks below.

Archibald did not interfere. He had seen the villains at work and that was enough.

After a few minutes the mischievous badgers disappeared as silently and suddenly as they had come.

Next morning Archibald called

an emergency meeting in Koalaville town hall. After a long discussion with his fellow citizens, Archie Duke the mayor decided that the Badgervillians should be severely punished.

The koalas sent a telegram to the wicked badgers telling them that on the following Sunday a great battle was to take place between them on the big beach halfway between Badgerville and Koalaville. The battle would begin early in the morning. Each side should come armed with whatever they could muster.

Archibald and his family had brooms.

Archie Duke brought boxes of old office files from the town hall to throw one after another at the badgers' heads.

PUBLIC RECORDS
INK
The battle lasted

TOP SECRET FILE
RECORD OF BIRTHS AND MARRIAGES

Archie Tect had plenty of weapons to choose from: spades, trowels, and bags of cement. He brought them all in his wheelbarrow.

Archie Vist came with a pile of old history books and magazines.

As for Archisoufflé, he brought as many pots and pans as he could carry.

On the badgers' side, they were equally well equipped to face the enemy.

Badjellyfish, the fisherman, brought his nets and a load of old fish.

Badgibberish brought all his unsold newspapers and some drums of printers' ink.

Badgiovanni came with his old music scores and some stage weapons borrowed from the opera house.

Badgenius took along some old Greek and Latin dictionaries,

and Badgick Carpet filled the boot of his car with all the old plaster busts and vases he had not been able to sell in his shop.

BOOK
12
CEMENT

all day

Little by little everything disappeared from sight. The sand rose in thick clouds, kicked up by the feet of the fierce opponents.

Around eight o'clock in the evening, the clashing and banging stopped. The clouds settled.

All the inhabitants of Wombalano, totally exhausted, had fallen asleep.

*

* *

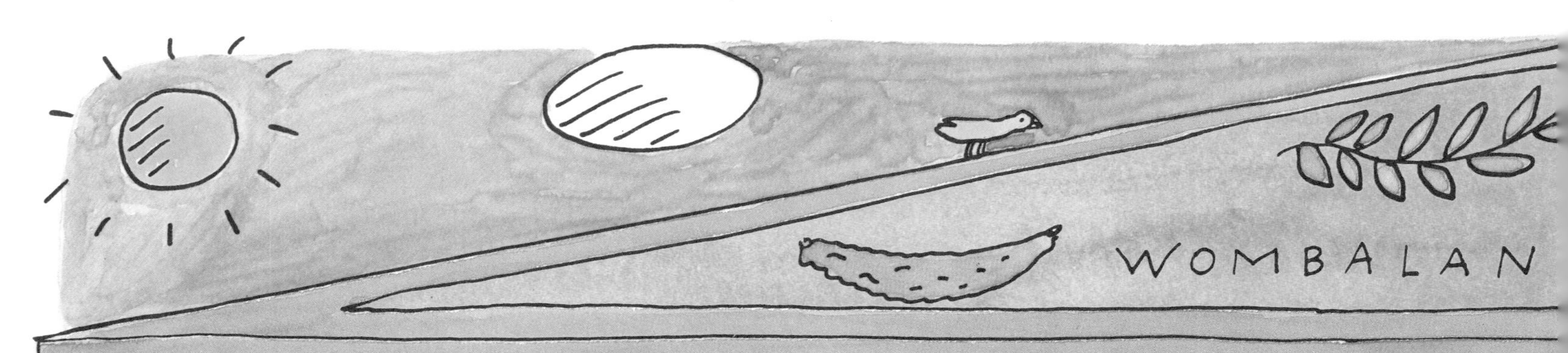

The opinion in Koalaville was that the badgers had got what they deserved, and everyone hoped that they would never do such a terrible thing again. In fact, this was the very promise that Badgibberish made when he appeared before Archie Duke the next morning to offer his apologies on behalf of all the Badgervillians.

Archie Duke, who was soft-hearted, forgave the badgers. He organized a grand ball that very evening to celebrate the end of their quarrel. During the celebration Archibald was awarded the Grand Order of the Eucalyptus.

Harmony reigned once more, and the koalas and badgers started again to play regular matches of rugby and basketball on the island of Wombalano.

The end

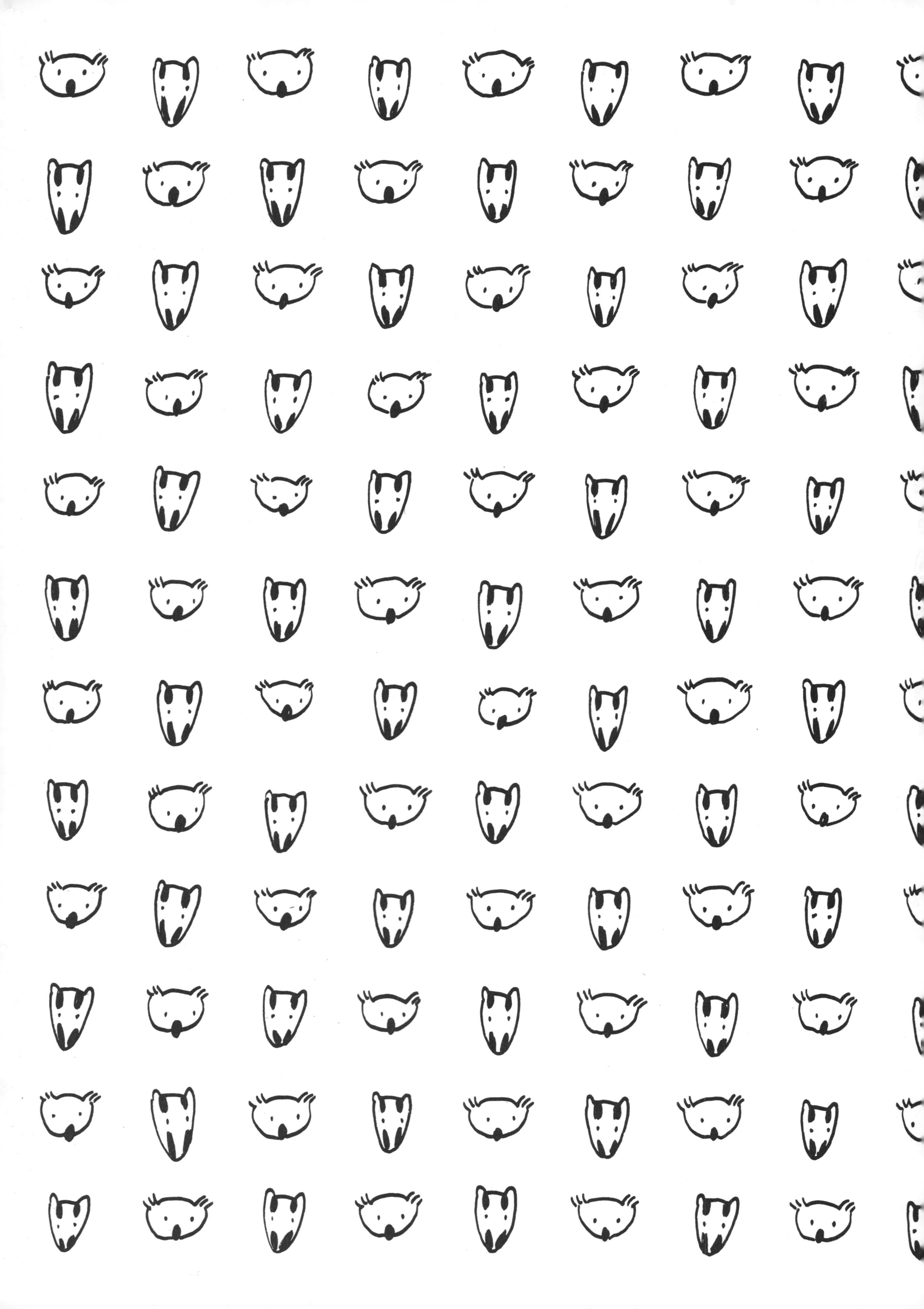